WAIST TRAINING 101

A
GUIDE TO USING
CORSETS TO SLIM YOUR
WAISTLINE

VANNA B.

HOPE
STREET
publishing

WAIST TRAINING 101: A Guide to Using Corsets to Slim Your Waistline by Vanna B.

http://www.WaistTraining101.com

ISBN: 978-0-9853515-4-0

Hope Street Publishing
P.O. Box 2705
Philadelphia, PA 19120
contact@hopestreetpublishing.com
http://www.HopeStreetPublishing.com

CONTENTS

Acknowledgements

I'd like to thank everyone that was a part of the creation of this book. RJ Jacques, for providing your amazing photography, design, and illustration services. Cover model Molly McKeon and fitness model Cantria Williams, for lending their beauty and talent. Rosemary Ashley, for perfecting the hair and make-up for the cover shoot. And last, but not least, Tahnee and The Passional for providing the beautiful corset pictured on the cover and assisting with the photo shoot. Thank you all for participating in this project and helping me bring *Waist Training 101* to fruition!

Disclaimer

The information presented in this book reflects the author's personal experiences and ongoing research into waist training and corsetry. Nothing in this book should be construed as a substitute for the medical advice of a physician, particularly with respect to any issue or symptom that may require diagnosis or medical attention. Always consult your doctor before beginning a waist training regimen.

1

INTRODUCTION TO
WAIST TRAINING

The Corset Comeback

Once considered a fashion staple for the ideal female form, the corset has made an astounding comeback, regaining widespread popularity thanks in part to celebrities like Jessica Alba, Beyoncé, Dita Von Teese, and Jennifer Garner. Women are once again lacing up daily with the goal of reshaping their bodies and cinching inches off their waistlines. This practice, known as waist training or corset training, is done all in the name of beauty, sex appeal, and the coveted hourglass figure.

Waist Training 101: A Guide to Using Corsets to Slim Your Waistline will provide you with a comprehensive, easy-to-follow crash course in preparing for and beginning your waist training journey. If you are not yet sure whether or not waist training is right for you, this book will give you the means to make an educated decision.

What is Waist Training?

Waist training is the wearing of a corset with the intention of semi-permanently* slimming and reducing the waist circumference. Regular wear of an appropriate steel boned corset can reshape the lower ribs and abdominal fat, in turn, gradually decreasing the waistline.

decrease

"Semi-permanently" meaning a reduction that remains after the corset is removed. In order to maintain an accomplished reduction, you must continue to wear the corset. Otherwise your waist will begin to expand back toward its natural size.

Waist Training vs. Tight Lacing

While people often use the terms interchangeably, tight lacing and waist training are not the same thing. Tight lacing is the wearing of a corset tied very tightly on the body to

> **Did You Know?**
> The saying "a loose woman" is said to have originated with Victorian-era prostitutes and the belief that a loose corset was a sign of a loose woman.

 copied from TLA?

2

achieve an instant, extreme reduction (while the corset is worn.) And while it is certainly possible for one to tight lace and waist train at the same time, every tight lacer is not necessarily waist training.

A History of Corsets

According to Valerie Steele, fashion historian, curator, and director of the Museum at the Fashion Institute of Technology, "The first true corsets date from some time in the first half of the sixteenth century, when aristocratic women began wearing 'whalebone bodies'…The style seems to have originated in Spain and/or Italy, and spread rapidly to other European countries." (chap. 1, "Steel and Whalebone: Fashioning the Aristocratic Body" pp. 6-7) The desire to keep the body stiff and controlled was a natural extension of the elite's inclination to appear regal, proud, and disciplined at all times.

> **Did You Know?**
> In the Victorian era, when going un-corseted was considered indecent, pregnant and postpartum women wore special maternity and nursing corsets.

These corsets, also called "stays," used "rigid materials, such as whalebone, horn, and buckram" for the boning. (chap. 1, p. 7) As in modern corsets, the boning located at center-front was called the busk. Busks were often adorned with decorative embellishments or phrases of love. Additional bones were eventually added to the sides. There were various types of corsets: open ones that laced up the front, and closed ones that laced up the back. There were plain ones intended to be worn as undergarments, and there were elaborate ones that were worn as outer clothing.

By the 1790s, empire waist dresses were becoming popular, and many women were abandoning boned stays for lighter, boneless corsets that only supported the breasts. But once the neoclassical fashion began to fade, boned corsets returned to be more popular than ever.

In the nineteenth century, corsets began to be worn under clothing only. The majority of them were back lacing with frontal busks, and they were usually plain white.

As more and more people began to believe corsets to be unhealthy, alternative "health corsets," such as the straight-front or S-bend corset of the Edwardian era, appeared. Although it was said to exert less pressure on the organs, the S-bend corset forced a more unnatural posture, which caused "balance difficulties and back pain." (chap. 3, "Dressed to Kill: The Medical Consequences of Corsetry" pp. 84-85)

The decline of the corset is said to have been brought about by the ideal silhouette changing from hourglass-shaped to long and slender. Where the corset was once a fashion staple, it was replaced by brassieres and elasticized shapewear such as hip-slimming girdles.

3

Waist Training and Your Health

Benefits of Corsets

More than likely, you are reading this book because you want to reduce your waistline by waist training with a corset. Waist training is a safer and more affordable way to reshape your body without undergoing cosmetic surgery. But there are also other, less obvious, benefits of corset wearing.

- **Improved Posture**

One of the results of regularly wearing a corset is improved posture. When worn, the rigid form of the garment causes the wearer to maintain a straight, upright posture, which in turn encourages them to build the habit of keeping their back straight even while the corset is off.

- **Preventing Back Injuries**

Because of the great support it provides the back, wearing a corset can also relieve back pain and help prevent back injuries. To bend while wearing a corset, the wearer must bend at the knees—the correct way—instead of bending at the waist, which can strain the back.

- **Correcting Diastasis Recti**

Wearing a corset also works as a remedy for an abdominal injury called diastasis recti, which many women experience after pregnancy. Also known as abdominal separation, diastasis recti occurs when the rectus abdominis muscle splits into two halves as a result of the stretching of the muscle by the growing baby. Separated abdominals can give your stomach a bloated, pushed out look. Corset wearing helps push the two halves of the muscle back in place, correcting the condition.

Health Concerns

For years people have debated over whether or not prolonged wear of a corset can pose health risks. Here are some of the most common concerns.

• **Organ Compression**

Arguments have been made that wearing a corset can compress and move the heart, lungs, liver, stomach, uterus, and other organs, bruising them and impairing the ways in which they function.

One counterargument commonly given is that our organs easily adapt to being gradually moved, as they do during pregnancy. When tightening a corset incrementally, as recommended, and refraining from trying to force extreme results in an unreasonable timeframe by tightening too much too quickly, the organs will adjust to your corseted body shape just as a pregnant woman's organs adjust to being moved around to accommodate a growing baby.

The fact is that no evidence has ever been furnished proving that corsets are harmful. The misconceptions widely believed today are myths dating back to the seventeenth through nineteenth centuries when corsets saw their rise to infamy.

11

In her book *The Corset: A Cultural History*, Valerie Steele unveils the findings of she and cardiologist Dr. Lynn Kutsche's research on corsets' effects on health.

Steele concludes, "The modern feminist critique of corsetry rests in large part on an uncritical acceptance of doctors' and dress reformers' claims about the medical dangers of corsetry." "….attempts to assess medical diagnoses from the past are fraught with difficulties, but from the perspective of modern medicine, corsets were extremely unlikely to have caused most of the diseases for which they were blamed." (chap. 3, pp. 67-68)

Instead, the diseases, which ranged from epilepsy and chlorosis to cancer and hysteria, can be attributed to malnutrition, misdiagnosis (physicians mistaking certain diseases for other, infectious ones), doctors' prejudices against corsets, and a general lack of knowledge.

The latter is evident in the fact that corsets were blamed for causing diseases, such as tuberculosis, in women, even though the same illnesses were seen in men who did not wear corsets.

> **Did You Know?**
> Victorian girls wore lighter, training corsets to prepare them for the adult corsets they would begin wearing as adolescents.

Likewise, it was discovered that damaged and displaced livers, spleens, and uteruses that were attributed to corset wearing were also found in working women who did not wear corsets.

Steele points out, "With few coherent and valid scientific theories to explain what caused most diseases, it was natural for nineteenth-century doctors to look for what seemed like plausible causes for the diseases they encountered." (chap. 3, p. 79)

"Indeed it is rather surprising that historians have been so reluctant to question accounts of corset-induced disease without considering the state of medical knowledge, clinical medicine, and the manifold biases of many physicians of the time." (chap. 3, p. 78)

In a healthy individual, the only proven health effects of the organs being compressed by a corset are decreased stomach and lung capacity, and slowed digestion, none of which are life-threatening conditions.

• Rib Damage

As with the organs and other body parts, rib damage is highly unlikely with incremental tightening and a proper fitting corset. The two lowest pairs of ribs are called the "floating" ribs because they do not connect to the sternum (breastbone.) They are the most flexible of all the ribs and gradually adjust to conform to the corset's shape.

• Muscle Atrophy

There are claims of waist trainers experiencing muscle atrophy as a result of their bodies becoming dependent on the support of the corset instead of allowing the abdominal muscles to support it.

Although muscle weakness is a rare occurrence with proper, gradual waist reduction, it is a good idea to follow a simple abdominal workout routine to help keep the muscles of the core strong and healthy, which will only assist with your waist training. (Suggested strength exercises and stretches can be found in Chapter 10.)

- **Skin Issues**

Some minor irritations that can possibly occur to the skin on your torso with frequent corset wear are dryness, chaffing, and calluses. Keeping your skin clean and moisturized will help keep it healthy. When using lotion, powder, or other skin products, be sure to apply them to your skin under your shirt or corset liner to keep the corset clean.

While rare, more serious skin issues, such as rashes, sores, and skin infections, are possible signs that your corset does not fit correctly.

Safety Precautions

Consult your doctor prior to beginning waist training. Your physician can evaluate your overall health and any preexisting conditions you may have to determine if waist training could further complicate them.

It is important to remember that waist training is a **gradual** process that should be done slowly, little by little over time. Always listen to your body. Pain, numbness, and difficulty breathing are signs that your corset is tied too tightly and needs to be loosened or removed. Trying to rush the process by tying your corset too tightly, wearing it for too long, or forcing it to lace too small too soon is dangerous and increases the risk of injury.

4

ANATOMY OF A CORSET

Bones (also called Stays) – The long, thin, flat inner rods that allow the corset to retain its shape by keeping it stiff and preventing it from wrinkling.

Busk – Used to open and close the corset in the front, the busk is made from two flat steel bones, one placed on each side of the corset opening. One side contains loops; the other contains the pins that lock into the loops.

Grommets (also called Two-Part Eyelets) – The round metal holes that laces are threaded through. They keep the laces from being damaged and prevent the laces damaging the fabric of the corset.

> **Did You Know?**
> Although controversial, with dandyism came the practice of men wearing corsets in attempts to appear more refined and aristocratic.

Waist Tape – A strip of sturdy fabric located inside the corset around the waist, where there is the most pressure. It reinforces the waistline, ensuring that the corset does not become stretched out.

Modesty Panel (also called a Lace Protector) – The piece of fabric that covers the gap left when a corset is not laced completely closed. It protects the wearer's back from burn as the laces are pulled tighter.

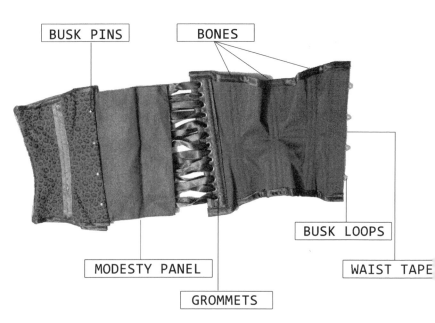

5

TYPES OF CORSETS

Corset Styles

Corsets are available in several styles:

- **Underbust**

Corsets that cover the torso only and begin just under the breasts. Underbusts are the most highly recommended type of corset for waist training.

> **Did You Know?**
> Corsets were primarily made by men up until sometime in the eighteenth century.

- **Overbust**

Corsets that support and cover the breasts. The majority of waist training aficionados do not recommend overbust corsets for beginning waist trainers.

• **Longline**

As the name suggests, longline corsets are longer and come down further on the hip. They are a good option for taller individuals who find regular length corsets too short for them.

• **Waist Cincher** (also called a Waspie) A shorter underbust corset, typically four to eight inches long, that cinches or nips in the

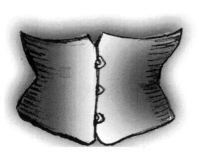

waist. A waist cincher is less restrictive than a full corset, allowing for more mobility. It is a good choice for beginners and those interested in light waist training, as well as shorter individuals who find regular length corsets too long for them.

Corset Shapes

Different silhouettes are provided by different corset shapes:

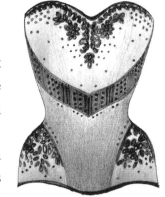

- **Conical**

A corset with a straight line from the top to the waist that gives it an inverted cone shape. This is considered an extreme shape and is not recommended for beginners.

- **Hourglass**

A subtly curved corset that primarily shapes the waist. This shape is a great choice for waist training beginners and those who desire to waist train but are not fond of the idea of

21

reshaping the ribcage.

- **Extreme Hourglass**

Like the classic hourglass, this corset shape fully accommodates the natural shape of the ribcage and hips. The extreme hourglass, however, features a dramatically drawn in waist, bearing the closest resemblance to an actual hourglass.

- **Pipe Stem**

A dramatic shape (sometimes also considered a more extreme version of the hourglass) in which the waist circumference is extended upwards, putting pressure on the lower ribcage. This style is only recommended for seasoned waist trainers.

- **S-Bend** (also called a Swan Bill, Straight Front, and Health Corset)

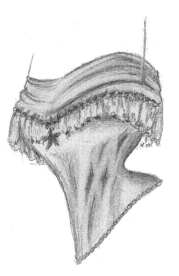

Its name derived from the S shape the body form takes on when looking at the wearer from the side. The front of S-bend corsets have extremely rigid fronts, which cause the torso to be thrust forward while the while the hips and derriere are thrust back in an unnatural form of posture.

- **Elizabethan and Victorian**

These are the historic corset forms that modern corset styles are based from. Period replicas from the Elizabethan and Victorian eras are commonly sought after for costumes, historical reenactments, and by corset aficionados and collectors.

Fabrics

In addition to being available in various types and shapes, corsets come in a variety of fabrics. Silk, satin, and leather are some of the various fashion fabrics available. For your main waist training corset, it is recommend that you choose one with a cotton, such as coutil, twill, or canvas, as its internal lining or strength layer. Cotton is a durable yet breathable fabric, making it a good choice for the long hours and heavy wear your corset will see over the course of its life.

6

CHOOSING THE
RIGHT CORSET

In addition to the shape, style, and fabric, there are
other factors to take into consideration when
selecting a waist training corset.

Off-the-rack vs. Custom Corsets
Off-the-rack corsets are ready-made ones sold as-is.
They are made with the goal of accommodating
"standard" proportions (average bust-waist-hip
ratio) to try to fit as many customers as possible.
Since the dimensions are predetermined, they will
not fit every body type perfectly, especially those
with not-so-average proportions. To get an idea of
how a particular corset may fit, check the
dimensions before purchasing and compare them to
your measurements.

Custom or bespoke corsets are made specifically to

accommodate your individual body. Although it is possible for many people to find an off-the-rack corset that suits them, a custom corset will always provide a better fit since it is made using your exact measurements. For this reason I do recommend investing in a custom corset for waist training if you are able to. Custom corsets are generally significantly more expensive than those purchased off the rack. The lowest price I have ever seen for a custom corset is $150, although it is more common to see them sold for $300 and up, as opposed to around $80 and up for a quality off-the-rack corset. Considering the amount of time you'll spend wearing it for waist training, a custom made corset is a great investment.

I offer a line of quality off-the-rack steel boned corsets at www.waisttraining101.com/corsets. Additionally, an up-to-date directory of other corsetieres and merchants providing off-the-rack and custom corsets is available at www.waisttraining101.com/directory.

What to Look for in a Corset

Prior to purchasing a corset, inspect it for the following components to ensure it is ideal for waist training:

- **Steel Bones**

A corset must be constructed with steel bones in order to be effective in reshaping the body. Corsets containing at least 20 bones (a combination of rigid flat bones and flexible spiral bones) are ideal, although corsets with fewer bones are sometimes used.

- **Laces**

A good, high-quality waist training corset tightens with sturdy laces. (Nylon, polyester, and double-sided satin are some of the stronger material options available.) Laces enable the wearer to adjust the corset as they please and keep it firmly tightened for the duration of its wear.

- **Busk**

In conjunction with laces, a frontal steel busk allows the wearer to easily put on and

27

remove the corset. This type of closure is used most often, although zippers are occasionally used as well. Hook and eye closures are not strong enough for use in waist training corsets. In addition to being able to withstand high tension, a steel busk flattens any lower tummy flab that may be present.

- **Waist Tape**

Located where tension is the highest, the waist tape reinforces the corset's waistline, ensuring that it does not become stretched out.

- **Sizing**

Quality corsets are sized by waist circumference in even-numbered inches (24, 26, 28, etc.) and never by S, M, L, etc.

- **Overall Quality**

Carefully inspect the corset for any defects or imperfections. If purchasing in person, pick it up and notice the weight. An extremely light corset may be an indication of plastic boning as steel bones are heavy. A steel-boned corset seldom weighs under a full pound. When laid flat, a squared shape instead of a curvy one, can signify a poor cut. Wrinkled fabric, as well as less obvious details like extremely crooked stitching or an inconsistent pattern, are further indications of questionable quality.

Garments Not Recommended for Waist Training

There are other types of shapewear that people often incorrectly assume are suitable for waist training. Girdles, fajas, sports shapers, and control tops are all undergarments that can be worn to **temporarily** slim and smooth the body. Commonly made of stretchy fabrics such as Spandex, Lycra, or Latex, they are less restrictive and offer only minor reductions while worn.

Did You Know?
The smallest waist ever recorded belonged to Ethel Granger. Her corseted waist measured a mere 13 inches.

Fashion corsets are those made to be worn as fashionable garments, but not suitable for waist training. Sometimes indistinguishable from quality waist training corsets to the untrained eye, many beginning waist trainers mistakenly purchase a fashion corset instead of a proper waist training corset. Fashion corsets are typically constructed with inferior quality fabrics and materials such as weaker metal grommets. They often use hook and eye, zipper, and/or basic ribbon lace-up closures. The main feature rendering these corsets useless for waist training is their plastic boning, which easily bends and breaks, making it incapable of providing enough pressure to alter the body in any permanent way.

All of the garments mentioned above are useless for waist training. Once removed, the body will immediately revert back to its original shape. They do not contain steel boning, thus they do not have the capabilities of causing any permanent or semi-permanent changes in body shape.

7

MEASURING

Whether you decide to purchase an off-the-rack style or go custom, it is important that you measure yourself correctly to ensure you select the right size corset. **A proper fit is imperative for successful waist training**.

When measuring, be sure not to suck your stomach in or push it out. You should pull the measuring tape taut, so that there are no wrinkles in it, but don't pull it tightly to where it is pulling you in.

You will need to take the following measurements:

- **Underbust** (Just under your breasts, where the band of your bra lies.)

- **Natural waist** (The smallest part of your waist, typically located several inches below your ribcage and about an inch above your navel.)

•   **Upper hip** (Around your hips along the line of the iliac crest. Not around the largest part of your hips or around your derriere.)

•   **Torso** (Vertical length from just under your bust to your seated lap.)

Additional measurements you may need:

•   **Bust** (Around the fullest part of your breasts.) If purchasing an <u>overbust</u> corset you will also need this measurement.

•   **Lower hip** (Around the largest part of your hips.) You will need this measurement if purchasing a <u>longline</u> corset.

> **Did You Know?**
> With a corseted waist circumference of 15 inches, Cathie Jung currently holds the title for the smallest waist on a living person.

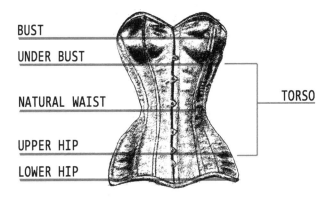

BUST
UNDER BUST
NATURAL WAIST
UPPER HIP
LOWER HIP
TORSO

When ordering a custom corset, your corset maker will require additional measurements and can assist you with where and how they should be taken.

Be sure to record your starting measurements and goal waist circumference on the Measurement Tracker on page 63.

If you have difficulties measuring yourself, enlist the help of a friend, corset maker, tailor, or seamstress. Inaccurate measurements could cause you to purchase the wrong size, and with an ill-fitting corset comes the risk of painful wear, injury, and damage to the garment.

Most corset makers and vendors recommend purchasing a corset four to five inches below your natural waist size. So if your waist circumference is 30 or 31 inches, you should order a size 26.

8

Beginning Waist Training

What to Wear Under Your Corset

It is recommended that you wear a layer of clothing between your skin and the corset. This will provide a barrier between any sweat, lotion, or perfume, helping to keep your corset clean. A thin layer of fabric can also lessen occurrences of chaffing. Although corset liners are sold, a camisole, tube top, tank, or other snug-fitting top will work just as well. Avoid baggy shirts that can wrinkle under the corset and interfere with fit.

> **Did You Know?**
> Perhaps the world's most well-known modern corsetier, the talented Mr. Pearl creates some of the most beautiful corsets ever made. His celebrity clientele list includes Madonna, Beyonce, Victoria Beckham, Kylie Minogue, and Dita Von Teese.

Lacing Your Corset

Most likely your corset will come with the laces

already in it. But if it does not, or if you desire to swap them out for a different set of laces, you will need to know how to properly insert them.

The vast majority of experienced waist trainers use a method of corset lacing known as bi-directional lacing. The name derives from the fact that both back to front and front to back lacing are used together. Unlike traditional lacing that follows one direction only, bi-directional lacing allows the corset to be laced completely closed, as there are no laces preventing it by crossing through the center. Bi-directional lacing allows the corset to be tightened more easily and enables the wearer to easily lace their own corset, which are other reasons it is the preferred lacing method.

Orchard Corset provides the following bi-directional lacing instructions:

1. Starting at the top, pull one side of the lace from back to front through the first two grommets. Pull the lace all the way through, ensuring the length is even on both sides.

2. Take the lace from the right side and feed it through the next grommet down on the left side from front to back. Repeat this for the left side. You should now have an X on the outside.

3. Take the lace from the right side and feed it through the next grommet on the left side from back to front. Repeat this step for the left side. You should now have an X on the inside of the corset below the first outer X.

4. Continue steps two and three until you reach the center of your corset (the narrowest point of your waist). The laces should now be on the outside of the corset.

5. Take the lace from the right side and feed it through the next grommet down on the same (right) side. Pull it partly through (approximately 18 inches of lace). Repeat for the left side. (These loops will be used to tighten and secure the corset closed.)

6.   Take the lace from the right side and feed it through the next grommet down on the left side from back to front. Repeat for the left side. This should give you another X on the inside.

7.   Resume the alternating inside and outside X pattern until you read the bottom of the corset.

8.   When you reach the bottom, tie the ends of the laces into a tight knot.

When you put your corset on, pull the outer X's to remove the slack in the laces. Start from the top and bottom of the corset and move toward the center, tightening the pull loops as you go along. Once the laces are tightened to your satisfaction, secure them by tying them in a bow. Do not wrap the lace ends around your waist. Doing so can damage the corset.

First Wear and Seasoning

Before lacing your corset tightly you must properly break it in. This process is known as seasoning. When first putting it on, make sure the corset's laces are thoroughly loosened and unhook the busk. Put your corset on, ensuring that it is on right side up. As you are putting it on, line the waist tape up with your natural waist (the smallest part of your waist.) Next, fasten the busk. Adjust the modesty panel, pulling it straight and flat across the gap under the laces. Then you can slightly tighten your corset.

Never pull the laces tightly before your corset is broken in. Doing so can cause damage to various parts of the corset and prevent it from fitting correctly. Breaking in your corset will help it mold to the shape of your body, allow your body to get accustomed to the corset, and prevent damage, and injury from improper fit.

The corset should be worn lightly snug for two hours every day for two weeks before further tightening it. After breaking it in, you can begin slowly tightening your corset in gradual increments.

Getting Started

Once your corset is thoroughly seasoned, you can begin waist training. You can now lace it snugly, but never so tightly that it is painful.

After a half hour of wear, you may slightly tighten your corset, if desired. By then the corset will have adjusted to your body, and your body to the corset, making a further reduction of ½ to 1½ inches possible.

Always be careful not to lace your corset too tightly. Listen to your body. If your ribs, stomach, or any other part of you begins to hurt, your corset is too tight. If you begin to experience numbness, tingling, dizziness, or difficulty breathing, your corset is too tight. Loosen it or remove it immediately.

Many beginners make the mistake of assuming that forcing their corset tighter will help them see results sooner. In actuality, the number of hours per day and the number of days per week that you wear your corset are the primary factors in determining how quickly you will see results. Therefore it is more beneficial to be able to wear the corset comfortably for a longer period of time than to lace it very tightly and have to remove it sooner due to discomfort.

Most experienced waist trainers wear their corsets for 6 to 18 hours a day, 5 to 7 days a week when aiming for a reduction, but you will find those who wear their corsets 23/7, only removing them to shower.

After seasoning your corset, you should start out wearing it 3 or 4 hours at a time and gradually work up to wearing it for longer periods of time.

Plan a waist training schedule that works around your lifestyle and daily activities. You can waist train while you're out running errands or while you're at school or work. If you will be wearing a corset at your job, and work in an office or other conservative atmosphere, you can conceal it under your clothing. Some people do almost everything in their corsets, including sleep. And although some opt to do light exercise while wearing their corsets, I do not recommend working out in your corset due to the reduced lung capacity experienced during wear.

Removing Your Corset

Just as when you are putting on your corset, it is important to loosen the laces before unhooking the busk closure to remove your corset. Trying to unfasten the busk while the laces are still tightened can cause damage to the corset's busk and bones. Loosen your corset by untying the bow. Then, starting closest to the center and working toward the ends, pull each of the X's until the corset hangs loosely on your body and you can easily unhook the busk without putting any strain on it.

9

DIET

It is strongly recommended that you incorporate exercise and a healthy diet into your waist training regimen.

Not only is eating a healthy, well-balanced diet good for your overall health; it can help you attain your waist training goals faster. If you have excess fat, you can trim some of the inches by changing your eating habits.

Counting Calories for Weight Loss

Calorie counting is the most common method used to lower food intake for weight loss. If you're like me, however, you may quickly grow weary of calculating and tallying the calories of all the food you consume. In my experience, after a couple weeks of using the calorie-counting method, I had a good grasp on what and how much I could eat to stay within my acceptable range. From then on it was more so about being mindful of what I ate and steering clear of sugary and fattening foods.

> **Did You Know?**
> As part of sexual fetishism, corsets are commonly used in bondage, discipline, and sadomasochistic activities.

In order to figure out how many calories you should consume daily to lose weight, you need to know your Basal metabolic rate (BMR). Your BMR is the amount of energy your body needs to function. We use about 60% of the calories we consume each day for basic bodily functions such as breathing. Other factors that influence your BMR are height, weight, age, and sex. Complete the following steps:

1.   Calculate your BMR using the appropriate formula below.

Women:
655 + (4.3 x weight in pounds) + (4.7 x height in inches) - (4.7 x age in years)

Men:
66 + (6.3 x weight in pounds) + (12.9 x height in inches) - (6.8 x age in years)

2.   Perform the following calculation to incorporate activity into your daily caloric needs.

- If you are sedentary: BMR X 20%
- If you are lightly active: BMR X 30%
- If you are moderately active (You exercise most days a week.): BMR X 40%
- If you are very active (You exercise intensely on a daily basis or for prolonged periods.): BMR X 50%
- If you are extra active (You do hard labor or are in athletic training.): BMR X 60%

3.   Add the result of the calculation above to your BMR. The result of this formula will be the number of calories you can eat every day to maintain your current weight. In order to lose weight, you'll need to take in fewer calories than this result.

As you lose weight, you can re-calculate the formula to assess your new BMR. (Scott, sec. 2, "Calculate Your BMR")

Eating While Corseted

If you eat while wearing your corset, it is likely you will consume less food than usual due to the corset compressing the stomach, limiting its capacity. You may find that the corset slows down your digestion and opt to remove it before eating. If you do eat while wearing your corset, eat slowly. Eating too fast or forcing yourself to eat too much, may cause discomfort. Eating smaller meals more frequently is ideal. If you usually eat three daily meals, try eating five or six smaller-portioned ones instead. Avoid foods that leave you gassy or constipated, as these are uncomfortable states to be in while wearing your corset. Consuming a high-fiber diet can help keep bowel movements regular and prevent constipation if you find that either of these become issues   for   you.

10

Exercise

Cardiovascular Exercise
Like dieting, cardiovascular exercise can help you achieve results sooner if you have excess unwanted fat. Exercising at 60-70% of your maximum heart rate (MHR) burns calories and fat, helping you lose weight and inches. Aim to do at least 30 minutes of cardio, three to four times a week. (The formulas below can be used to get an estimate of you MHR.)

Women: 216-[1.09 X Age]

Men: 202-[.55 X Age]

Strength Exercises
One of the health concerns arising from the extended wear of corsets is that the muscles in the back and

> **Did You Know?**
> In the Victorian era, special corsets were made for wear during every type of sport women took part in. These included tennis, swimming, horseback riding, and bicycling.

abdomen can become weakened due to them not being used while the corset is supporting the core. Doing some basic strength exercises will help keep the muscles of the back and core strong and healthy. Below are some great, effective moves to strengthen your abs and back simultaneously. They are quick and easy, will not interfere with your waist training, and can be done at home with nothing more than a yoga mat or towel to lie on. Perform these exercise moves at least two to three times per week, and follow them with the abdominal stretches listed. Remember to take your corset off before exercising.

- **The Plank**

1.   Get into a basic push-up position, only resting on your forearms (instead of your

hands) and toes.

2.   Hold your body in a stiff, straight line,
      making sure not to allow any part of your
      body to curve or sag. Hold for 30 seconds ,
      then rest for 30. Repeat two more times.

- **Bicycle Crunches**

1.   Lie on your
      back with
      your knees
      bent and feet
      flat on the
      floor. Lift
      your head,
      shoulders,
      and upper
      back off the
      floor and
      bend your
      arms so that
      your elbows

point out to the sides and your fingertips are
lightly touching your ears. (Do not grab your

head. It will encourage you to pull your head, which can injure your neck and back.)

2. Squeezing your abdominals, simultaneously move your right elbow and left knee toward each other while straightening your right leg. (Don't let it touch the ground).

3. Draw your right knee back up and immediately move your left elbow and right knee toward each other while straightening your left leg. That's one rep. Continue to move continuously, as if pedaling a bicycle. Do three sets of 15 reps. (Health.com, "How to Properly Do a Bicycle Crunch")

- **Abdominal Crunches**

1. Lying flat on your back, bend your knees and place your feet flat on the floor.

2. Bend your arms so that your elbows point out to the sides and your fingertips are lightly touching your ears. (Do not grab your head. It will encourage you to pull your head, which can injure your neck and back.)

3. Squeezing your abdominals, slowly lift your upper body off the floor and toward your knees until your shoulder blades are no longer touching the floor.

4.   Hold at the top for several seconds, then slowly lower your upper body back down to the starting position. Perform three sets of 20 reps.

• **Leg Raises**

1.   Lie flat on your back with your legs straight and together. (Keep legs together for the entire exercise.) Hands can be laid palms-down on the floor beside you, or if you prefer, you can place them under your hips for added support.

2. Squeezing your abdominal muscles, slowly lift your legs until they are perpendicular (at a 90-degree angle) to the floor.

3. Slowly lower your legs back down until they almost touch the ground. Perform three sets of 15 reps.

As your muscles get stronger, you can increase the number of repetitions as you see fit.

Stretches

These stretches will stretch the muscles in your core and back, preventing them from becoming stiff.

- **Bow Pose**

1. Lie face down on the floor with your knees bent.

2. Raise your head, chest, and legs off the floor and arch your back.

3. With your arms straight, grab your ankles, look up at the ceiling, and hold. (To increase the stretch, raise your legs toward the ceiling

and push your heels away from your glutes.) (Miller, sec. 2, "Bow Pose")

- **Rotating Stomach Stretch**

1. Lie on your stomach with your legs straight on the floor and your toes pointing away from you. Place your hands on the floor next to your shoulders with your fingers pointing forward.

2. Push your arms straight and raise your upper body off the floor. Bend your right arm and

twist your torso to the right. Hold. You will feel your left side stretching.

3. Repeat on the other side. (Miller, sec. 3, "Rotating Stomach Stretch")

11

Corset Care

Airing Out Your Corset

Always allow your corset to air out after you take it off. Once you remove it, hang it over a hanger with the lining facing up in a well-ventilated area away from direct sunlight. This will allow the fabric to breathe and help keep your corset cleaner longer.

> **Did You Know?**
> In the nineteenth century, couches with a high raised back on one side came to be known as fainting couches. Many houses and hotels also had fainting rooms where tightly corseted women could rest and catch their breath.

It is a good idea to have more than one corset of the same size, especially if you are waist training daily. Alternating between two or more corsets will allow for additional breathing time between wears.

Corset Storage

For long-term storage, there are several ways you

can store your corset. Some people prefer to roll their corsets up and store them on a closet shelf. Some store them lying flat in a dresser drawer, while others opt to hang theirs. Corset storage bags are sold as well, although they are not necessary for safe storage. Make sure that wherever you store your corset, it is kept away from direct sunlight, which can cause damage to the fabric.

Cleaning

When necessary, gently spot clean your corset using a mild detergent. Have it dry cleaned when it is in need of a good cleaning. **Never** place your corset in a washing machine or dryer as this could cause serious damage.

12

RESULTS

The most frequently asked question among beginning waist trainers is "How long will it be before I start to see results?" Unfortunately, there is no definitive answer to this question. Results and how quickly they will become evident depends on the individual and various factors:

Factors that Determine Results

- **Age** – Our skeletons become less flexible as we age.

- **Diet** – Your diet affects fat, muscle, hydration, and other factors that can contribute to how soon you see results.

- **Exercise** – Burning fat shaves inches off your waist.

- **Ribcage flexibility** – Some people's ribs are more flexible than others' and will begin to conform to the shape of the corset more quickly.

- **Percentage of body fat and muscle** – Fat is softer and therefore more malleable than muscle.

- **How often and how long you wear your corset** – Those corseting more frequently and for longer periods of time will likely see results sooner.

Sizing Down

Once you are able to lace your corset completely closed and wear it comfortably for an extended period of time on a regular basis, it is time to get a smaller size. Moving to the next size down is ideal, although some people will find they are able to move down two sizes.

Maintenance Corseting

When you can close your corset completely and do not wish to reduce your waistline any further, congratulations! You have successfully met your waist training goal. Once you achieve your goal waist circumference you will need to continue wearing your corset in order to maintain it. If you stop wearing it altogether, your waist

> **Did You Know?**
> Historically the ideal female proportions have been a bust and hip circumference close in size with a waist circumference about 10 inches smaller (for example, 35-25-35.)

will begin to revert back to its original shape. You will also need to maintain your weight, as gaining weight will add inches onto your waist.

How often it will be necessary to wear your corset for maintenance will vary from person to person. A good place to start is wearing it about half as often as you wore it while reducing. I suggest continuing to measure your waist regularly (weekly or bi-weekly), recording your measurements on the Measurement Tracker on page 63, and using the Waist Training Log on page 65 to keep track of how often and how long you wear your corset. If you notice your waist beginning to expand, adjust accordingly by wearing your corset more.

Conclusion

It is important to remember that ultimately, your results will depend on you. A corset alone is not enough; **your unwavering dedication and consistency are necessary components in bringing about the changes you wish to see**.

These changes will not become evident overnight, so be prepared to be patient. Few may notice a reduction in as little as three months. For others, it will take over a year. Keep track of your results by recording your measurements, and allow your progress along the way to motivate you. In the end, achieving your waist training goals will be a satisfying reward for all your hard work and diligence.

MEASUREMENT TRACKER

Record your measurements here. For a diagram and descriptions of all measurements, refer to Chapter 7.

Goal waist circumference _____

Date _____	Date _____
Bust _____	Bust _____
Underbust _____	Underbust _____
Natural Waist _____	Natural Waist _____
Upper Hips _____	Upper Hips _____
Lower Hips _____	Lower Hips _____
Torso _____	Torso _____
Date _____	Date _____
Bust _____	Bust _____
Underbust _____	Underbust _____
Natural Waist _____	Natural Waist _____
Upper Hips _____	Upper Hips _____
Lower Hips _____	Lower Hips _____
Torso _____	Torso _____
Date _____	Date _____
Bust _____	Bust _____
Underbust _____	Underbust _____
Natural Waist _____	Natural Waist _____
Upper Hips _____	Upper Hips _____
Lower Hips _____	Lower Hips _____
Torso _____	Torso _____

Date	_____		Date	_____
Bust	_____		Bust	_____
Underbust	_____		Underbust	_____
Natural Waist	_____		Natural Waist	_____
Upper Hips	_____		Upper Hips	_____
Lower Hips	_____		Lower Hips	_____
Torso	_____		Torso	_____
Date	_____		Date	_____
Bust	_____		Bust	_____
Underbust	_____		Underbust	_____
Natural Waist	_____		Natural Waist	_____
Upper Hips	_____		Upper Hips	_____
Lower Hips	_____		Lower Hips	_____
Torso	_____		Torso	_____
Date	_____		Date	_____
Bust	_____		Bust	_____
Underbust	_____		Underbust	_____
Natural Waist	_____		Natural Waist	_____
Upper Hips	_____		Upper Hips	_____
Lower Hips	_____		Lower Hips	_____
Torso	_____		Torso	_____
Date	_____		Date	_____
Bust	_____		Bust	_____
Underbust	_____		Underbust	_____
Natural Waist	_____		Natural Waist	_____
Upper Hips	_____		Upper Hips	_____
Lower Hips	_____		Lower Hips	_____
Torso	_____		Torso	_____

WAIST TRAINING LOG

Keep track of your waist training here.

Date	Inches Cinched	Time Worn	Notes

Date	Inches Cinched	Time Worn	Notes

QUICK REFERENCE GLOSSARY

Bones (also called **Stays**) – The long, thin, flat inner rods that allow the corset to retain its shape by keeping it stiff and preventing it from wrinkling.

Busk – Used to open and close the corset in the front, the busk is made from two flat steel bones, one placed on each side of the corset opening. One side contains loops; the other contains the pins that lock into the loops.

Conical – A corset shape in which there is a straight line from the top to the waist that gives it an inverted cone shape. This considered an extreme shape and is not recommended for beginners.

Corset – A garment worn on the torso that, when tightly drawn, can shape and mold the figure.

Corsetiere (also called a **Corsetier** or **Corset Maker**) – One who specializes in making corsets.

Corset Liner – A tube-shaped piece of fabric designed to be worn under a corset to protect the skin as well as the corset.

Corsetry – The art of making corsets and their components.

Coutil – A strong, non-stretching twill fabric with a tight herringbone weave made specifically for use in corsets.

Extreme Hourglass – A corset shape that dramatically draws in the waist while fully accommodating the natural shape of the ribcage and hips. This is the shape that most closely resembles an actual hourglass.

Floating Ribs – Ribs that are not attached to the sternum. In most people the eleventh and twelfth (lowest) rib pairs are floating ribs.

Grommets (also called **Two-Part Eyelets**) – The round metal holes that laces are threaded through.

They keep the laces from being damaged and prevent the laces damaging the fabric of the corset.

Hourglass – A subtly curved corset that primarily shapes the waist. A great choice for waist training beginners and those who desire to waist train but are not fond of the idea of reshaping the ribcage. This style is the ideal choice for those new to waist training.

Iliac Crest – The top border of the ilium, which is the largest and most prominent bone in the pelvis.

Longline – A longer corset that comes down further on the hip and is a good option for taller individuals who find regular length corsets too short for them.

Low Hip – The largest part of your hips. The low hip measurement is necessary when purchasing a longline corset.

Maintenance Corseting – Regular wear of a corset to retain the current waist circumference.

Modesty Panel (also called a **Lace Protector**) – The piece of fabric that covers the gap left when a corset is not laced completely closed. It protects the wearer's back from burn as the laces are pulled tightly.

Muscle Atrophy – The weakening and eventual wasting away of muscles due to them not being utilized.

Natural Waist – The smallest part of the waist, located several inches below the ribcage and about an inch above the navel.

Off-the-Rack (also called **Ready-to-Wear)** – A ready-made corset constructed with the goal of accommodating as many customers as possible.

Overbust – A corset that supports and covers the breasts.

Pipe Stem – A dramatic corset shape in which the waist circumference is extended upwards, putting pressure on the lower ribcage. This style is only recommended for seasoned waist trainers.

S-Bend (also called the **Swan Bill**, **Straight Front**, and **Health Corset**) – An extreme corset shape that causes the torso to be thrust forward while the hips and derriere are thrust back in an unnatural form of posture.

Seasoning – The process of gradually breaking in a new corset by wearing it lightly laced, allowing it to adapt to the body's shape.

Sizing Down – Switching to a smaller-sized corset once able to fully close your current size.

Tight Lacing – The wearing of a corset tied very tightly.

Underbust – A corset that covers only the torso and begins just under the breasts. An underbust is the best kind of corset to use for waist training.

Waist Cincher (also called a **Waspie**) – A shorter underbust corset, typically four to eight inches long, that cinches or nips in the waist.

Waist Tape – A strip of sturdy fabric located inside

the corset around the waist, where there is the most pressure. It reinforces the waistline, ensuring that the corset does not become stretched out.

Waist Training (also called **Corset Training**) – The wearing of a corset with the intention of semi-permanently reducing the waist circumference.

Upper Hips – Along the line of the iliac crest. Not around the largest part of your hips or derriere.

BIBLIOGRAPHY

Miller, Sarka-Jonae. "Abdominal stretching exercises." *Livestrong.com.* http://www.livestrong.com/article/98690-abdominal-stretching-exercises/.

Scott, Jennifer R. "How to Calculate Your Caloric Needs and Lose Weight." *About.com.* http://weightloss.about.com/od/eatsmart/a/blcalintake.htm.

Steele, Valerie. *The Corset: A Cultural History.* New Haven & London: Yale University Press, 2001.

"Corset Care & Lacing." *Orchardcorset.com.* http://www.orchardcorset.com/corset-care-lacing/.

"Calculate Your Maximum Heart Rate." *DigitFit.com.* http://www.digifit.com/heartratezones/maximum-heart-rate.asp.

"How to Properly do a Bicycle Crunch."
Health.com.
http://www.health.com/health/article/0,,20412214,0
0.html.

ABOUT THE AUTHOR

A native of Philadelphia, Vanna B. is an award-winning author of four Amazon best-sellers.

Vanna's interest in waist training originated with her using a steel boned corset to correct abdominal separation caused by a pregnancy. Once healed, she decided to continue wearing corsets to further reduce her waistline, and so began her research and exploration of the subject.

Vanna soon began diligently waist training, bringing her friends, colleagues, and followers along for the journey via photos and updates on social networks. Endless were the questions and curiosities her corsets drew, both online and from people who would stop her on the street when wearing them.

She wrote and published *Waist Training 101: A Guide to Using Corsets to Slim Your Waistline* with the hopes of educating and guiding beginning waist trainers, as well as helping to dispel common myths and misconceptions surrounding the practice.

Connect with Vanna on social networking sites:
www.facebook.com/vannabonline
www.twitter.com/msvannab
www.instagram.com/waisttraining101